Compost the Cat

Written by Nicola Wood

Illustrated by Lesley Thurlbeck

Compost the Cat!

Nicola Wood

I wish to personally thank the following people for their contributions to helping create this book. My illustrator, Lesley Thurlbeck, who has created all these lovely images throughout this book. Thank you Lou Grosart who gave me so much advice and support throughout my journey.

Darren Wright, Chris Kendall and CSSEF have helped me to make this book accesible for everyone. Also, a huge thank you to everyone who believed in me becoming a children's author.

www.theadventuresofcompost.co.uk

First published 2021 by The Adventures of Compost Limited.

Registered Address: Communications House,Lintonville Terrace, Ashington, Northumberland, NE63 9UN.

Registered Company Number:13433375

A CIP catalogue record for this book is available from the British Library.

ISBN: 978-1-8381093-0-1

Printed in United Kingdom

Compost is a cheeky cat,
Look here, he's saying hello!
He wants to show you where he lives,
We'll follow him; let's go!

He lives in a big plant pot.
On this big and grassy mound.
In front of a tall windmill,
with lovely views all around.

Compost hears the windmill spinning:
Whooshing in the breeze.
Feeling happy to start the day.
He leaps to the ground with ease.

SQUELCH and SQUASH his playful paws
walk along a muddy trail.
Listening to woodland calls,
as he swishes his black tail.

He stands tall and spins around.
Compost grumbles, "Ouch that hurt!"
Lying there is something strange,
Deep in mud and dusty dirt.

Compost is suprised to see,
A ginger cat in his way.
She has three little fluffy paws
and looks eager to play.

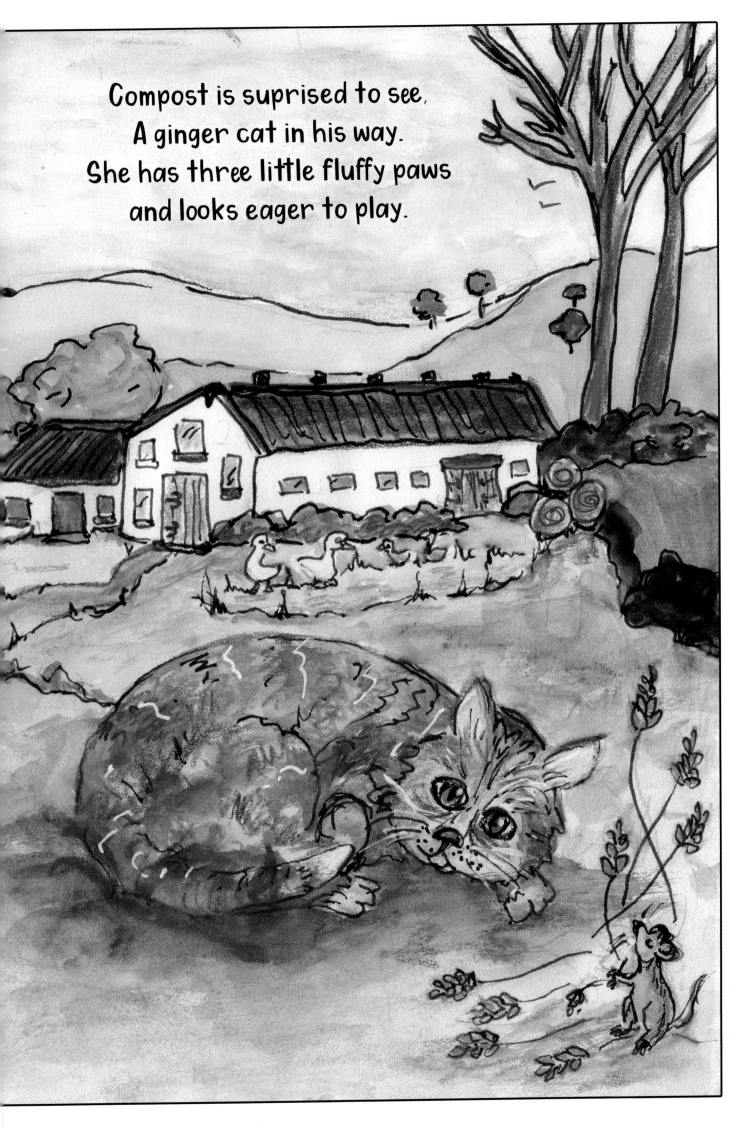

Jumping up and leaping quick,
He says "Compost is my name."

"Hello Compost, I'm Poppy,
I'm so glad that you came."

The cats go on a journey
Along the dusty track.
Spotting a river below
They hear the ducks go 'Quack!'

Down at the deep blue water's edge.
Compost plays on lily pads,
But Poppy watches closely and
starts to feel very sad.

"I really want to play with him"
Poor Poppy feels a shiver.
"But I am really scared,
Of this deep blue river."

She sees Compost having fun.
"I want to come and join you."

Feeling brave, she starts to run.
"Watch out, I'm coming through."

The cats play in the water,
With noisy splashing sounds.
Catching flies and seeing the fish.
Getting wet, splashing around.

They jump out of the water
and walk up the riverside.
Shaking droplets off their fur,
and waving their tails with pride.

Compost prances through the grass,
"Poppy, will you come and play?"
Poppy smiles at Compost,
"Yes, but you can lead the way"

Compost hides in the grass.
While Poppy counts, one and two.

Boys and girls, where has he gone?
Poppy says, "I'll find you."

LT

Playing together is great,
It's what they love to do.

Poppy jumps on Compost's back.
She smiles and laughs, "BOO."

They see some bushy hedges
Jumping over them ...one, two, three.
Poppy points to a big field,
"There is my home-come and see!"

Two happy cats, cuddle up
on a cushion of red flowers.
Smiling from cheek to cheek,
They chat and laugh for hours.

Starting a great adventure
is what good friends like to do.
Poppy jumps from the flowers,
"Today's been great with you."

As the daylight goes away,
Stars appear shining bright.
Birds nesting to fall asleep,
The cats hug and say "Goodnight."

Morning comes and birds tweet.
The cats wake to a sunny day.
They are pleased they found each other.
They stretch all ready to play.

Great adventures with each other,
Are all exciting and new.
Having fun together,
Will you be Compost's friend too?

Poppy Pairs

Can you find Poppy
and her matching pair?
Oh no, Look......
someone is over there!

Can Poppy find Compost?

To get ready for another adventure?

There are mice hiding in this book,
Can you find them?
Come on, let's take a look.

The illustrators initials, (LT)
are on each page,
Can you find them for me?

Compost was happy finding a new friend,
Poppy was really scared of the river.
How do you feel today?

Why do you think
Poppy has 3 legs?

Compost and Poppy
become good friends,
What makes a good friend?